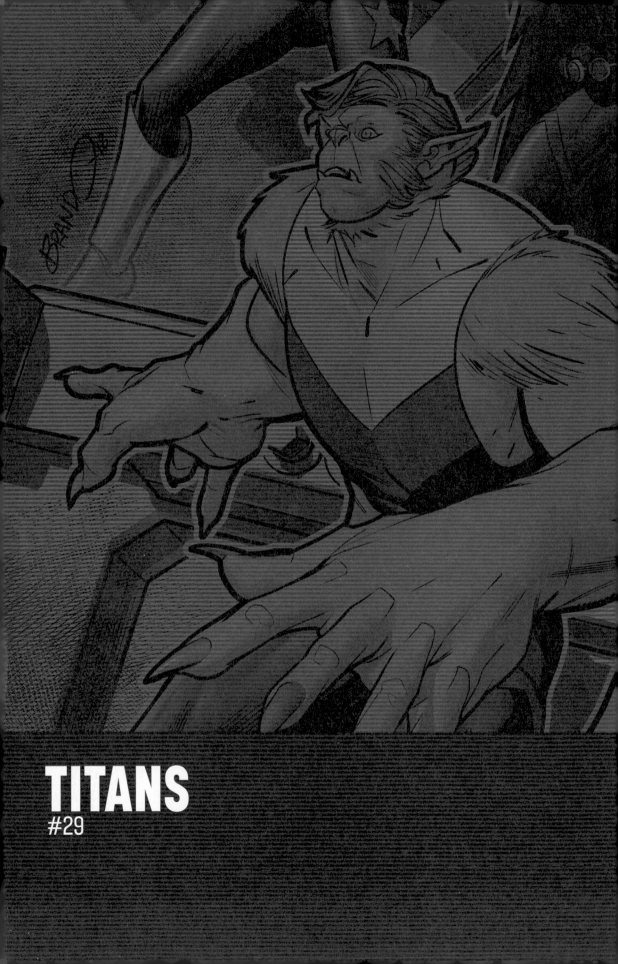

TITANS
#29

BB-BOOOM!

THH-WW

SSKKNRRKRKKKCHH!

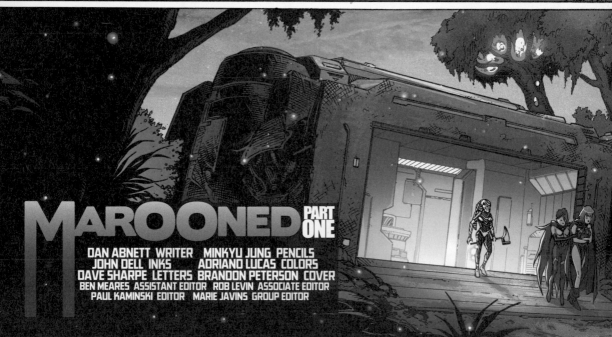

MAROONED PART ONE

DAN ABNETT WRITER   **MINKYU JUNG** PENCILS
JOHN DELL INKS   **ADRIANO LUCAS** COLORS
DAVE SHARPE LETTERS   **BRANDON PETERSON** COVER
BEN MEARES ASSISTANT EDITOR   ROB LEVIN ASSOCIATE EDITOR
PAUL KAMINSKI EDITOR   MARIE JAVINS GROUP EDITOR

ON THE BRIGHT SIDE, WE'RE NOT DEAD.

THAT'S A PRETTY LOW BAR FOR A BRIGHT SIDE.

DONNA, THAT DATA WE SCOOPED FROM THE OCEAN LORD'S SHIP IS *VITAL* TO THE SALVATION OF EARTH.

WE HAVE TO GET HOME AND *DELIVER* IT TO THE JUSTICE LEAGUE OR--

I HAVE A HUNCH THEY'LL HAVE TO *MANAGE* WITHOUT US.

HEY, MY UNCLE IS BACK THERE. THE ENTIRE *PLANET* COULD BE DESTROYED FOR ALL WE--

I'M SORRY, WAS *I* THE ONE DRIVING THE SHIP?

WHY DO YOU HAVE TO BE SUCH A--

--Y'KNOW WHAT? FORGET IT.

I'M GOING TO TRY AND FIX THE EMERGENCY BEACON. MAKE SOME REPAIRS.

DO *SOMETHING* USEFUL.

THERE IS A *PRACTICAL* WAY OF DETERMINING OUR PRESENT LOCATION. A *VISUAL* FIX.

EARTH MAY BE-- COMPARATIVELY--CLOSE, IN WHICH CASE I COULD CARRY US AND THE BOOM ROOM BACK--

I *SAW* THE HIT YOU TOOK IN THE BOOM ROOM, MISS M.

YOU'RE NOT CARRYING *ANYTHING*.

UHHHNNNN!

THEY WERE RIGHT. THE PAIN IS UNBEARABLE.

I HAVE OVERTAXED MY INJURY. I SHOULDN'T HAVE--

...

SHE CAN SURVIVE A FALL LIKE THAT, RIGHT?

RIGHT?

AND SHE'S GOING TO HIT HARD. WE HAVE TO GET TO HER.

OH CRAP.

SHE'S IN FREEFALL.

SHE BLACKED OUT.

HURRY!

DONNA?

YEAH. COMING.

THIS IS GETTING WORSE BY THE SECOND.

GUYS? GUYS! FOUND HER!

OUR ILLUSTRIOUS JUSTICE LEAGUE LIAISON. SHE WAS SUPPOSED TO BE THE RESPONSIBLE ONE.

NOW SHE'S ACTING AS RECKLESSLY AS THE REST OF US.

M'GANN?

GEEZ, SHE'S A MESS.

M'GANN! DAMN IT, WHERE ARE YOU?!

IT'S USELESS.

I'M USELESS.

ALL THE WORK WE'VE DONE TO SAVE THE WORLD...AND FOR WHAT?! WE CAN'T EVEN SAVE OURSELVES!

DAMN IT!

DAMN IT!

THIS IS THE DATA YOU TOOK FROM THE OCEAN LORD'S SHIP?

YEAH. IT'S *WAY BEYOND* HUMAN LEVELS. *SUPER* ADVANCED.

THE BOOM DRIVE IS WRECKED *BEYOND* REPAIR, BUT MAYBE USING *THIS* I CAN BUILD A *DIFFERENT* SYSTEM TO GET US BACK.

JUST... INVENT A WHOLE *NEW* INTERSTELLAR DRIVE SYSTEM?

NAT, WHEN WAS THE LAST TIME YOU SLEPT? OR ATE? OR DRANK SOMETHING?

YEAH, LET ME JUST FIX THAT *VENDING MACHINE*...

HAR. HAR.

I'LL REST SOON.

BUILDING A NEW DRIVE SYSTEM OUT OF THE SCRAPS WE HAVE WILL BE *DEMANDING*, EVEN *WITH* THE ALIEN DATA.

DAMN.

I CAN'T GET THE MAIN SENSORS BACK UP.

WE'LL HAVE TO LOOK FOR GAR THE OLD-FASHIONED WAY. I'LL HEAD OUT WITH RAVEN.

THERE IS *ONE* THING I'VE BEEN ABLE TO JURY-RIG.

GOOD A TIME AS *ANY* TO TEST IT.

I'VE REPAIRED THE DISTRESS BEACON.

AND *BOOSTED* ITS SIGNAL.

KLEKK!

GGRRRHHWWLLL!

GARFIELD! STOP!

OH &%$@, HE'S SO STRONG! HE'S GONE WAY FURTHER THAN I'VE EVER SEEN HIM--

RRAAAHHWOOLL!

=UGGGKK!=

NGHH!

WHUMMMMMMMPD!

I DON'T WANT TO HURT YOU, GAR.

HAMMER!

BRGGRRRLL!

BRRAAAHNGGGHHH!

WHH-RAFF!

WHHH-TANNGG!

OH GEEZ, HIS STRENGTH IS OFF THE CHARTS--

WHAMM!

SSKRAKKTT!

UOOB-WOOOB-WOOOB-WOOOB **UOOOB-WOOOB-WOOOB-WOO**

IT'S THE LIGHT... THE PULSE...

...IN HIS ENRAGED STATE, HE'S DRAWN TO THE BEACON...

GRRRRGGG!

GARFIELD!

"I MUST CALM HIM DOWN."

PLEASE, GARFIELD... PLEASE...

LISTEN TO MY VOICE. LISTEN TO MY PSIONICS. BE CALM.

J'GELZZ TEETH! I CAN BARELY STAND

THAT'S IT! CALM, GARFIELD LOGAN. BE CALM...

GRRRLL?

WHUNNNNTTT!

GWHHH!

Ooww...

AH CRAP! HE'S GOING FOR THE BOOM ROOM--

WOOOB-WOOOB-WOOOB

BBROOWWWLLL!

SHH! KA KKR SSKKR

WOOOB-WOOOB-WO

THR RUUNNGHH!

OB-WMB-WNNT-WNNT

SKKKRUNCHH!

THE BEACON--!

OH, BEAST BOY.

NO.

TITANS
#30

GRRRAAAAAGHHHH!

MAROONED PART TWO

DAN ABNETT WRITER   MINKYU JUNG PENCILS

JOHN DELL, SCOTT HANNA INKS

ADRIANO LUCAS, HI-FI COLORS   DAVE SHARPE LETTERS

BEN OLIVER & ROMULO FAJARDO JR. COVER

ROB LEVIN ASSOCIATE EDITOR   PAUL KAMINSKI EDITOR

MARIE JAVINS GROUP EDITOR

HOW CAN *THAT* BE MISS MARTIAN?

I DON'T UNDERSTAND. ISN'T SHE A GREEN MARTIAN LIKE J'ONN?

AREN'T WHITE MARTIANS SUPPOSED TO BE... KIND OF *EVIL?*

I...I...

WHATEVER THE CASE, WE HAVE TO BREAK THEM UP BEFORE THEY *KILL* EACH OTHER. I--

OWWW.

STOP THIS! **NOW!**

IS THAT... IS THAT *MISS MARTIAN?*

YOU'RE HURT, RAVEN. STEEL... WITH ME.

I HAVE *HAD* IT WITH THIS $%¢& TEAM!

I AM A *WHITE MARTIAN.* I KNOW THE *TERROR* THAT THE SIGHT OF ONE PROVOKES. THE FEAR. THE SUSPICION.

I *HIDE* MY TRUE SELF SO HUMANS WON'T *DESPISE* ME!

MMHH-GUNNN?

STOP HER! SHE'S GOING TO FRY HIS *BRAIN--*

NO. WAIT--

NGGHHH!

GARFIELD, DO YOU REMEMBER *TYLER?* DO YOU REMEMBER HOW YOU *SOOTHED* HIM? YOU SHOWED HIM *YOUR* TRUE SELF.

SHOWED HIM THERE WAS *NOTHING* TO BE AFRAID OF.

YOU LOOKED LIKE A MONSTER, BUT YOU *WEREN'T.* NOT INSIDE.

LOOK AT ME. I, TOO, LOOK LIKE A MONSTER.

BUT I AM *NOT.* NOT WHERE IT *COUNTS.*

PLEASE, GARFIELD. YOU DON'T HAVE TO *BE* WHAT OTHERS PERCEIVE YOU AS.

I'M SO SORRY. I RUINED EVERYTHING.

NAH, YOU HAVEN'T--

I *DID*. LOOK AT THE BOOM ROOM.

ALL YOUR REPAIRS... THE *BEACON*... THAT WAS SUPPOSED TO SAVE US.

I CAN *RE*-REPAIR. FORAGE FOR SPARES. THERE'S PLENTY OF WOOD.

WOOD?

HEY, IF ROBINSON CRUSOE CAN BUILD A CONDO OUT OF *BAMBOO*, I'M *SURE* I CAN--

STEEL!

IT WAS A JOKE, GAR. REMEMBER THOSE?

SERIOUSLY, I CAN *FIX* IT. I CAN GET THE BEACON WORKING AGAIN.

I DON'T KNOW WHAT HAPPENED. I JUST... I JUST *LOST* IT.

IT'S ALL THIS SOURCE ENERGY THAT'S INSIDE ME... THE STUFF THAT TURNED ME INTO *THIS*. I'VE BEEN BATTLING FOR WEEKS TO KEEP IT INSIDE.

CONCENTRATING ALL THE TIME TO KEEP MY POWERS AND MYSELF IN CHECK.

BUT WITH EVERYTHING THAT'S HAPPENED... I JUST...

...SOMETHING *SNAPPED*. I FELT MYSELF SLIDING. I COULDN'T *STOP* IT.

THEN IT WAS JUST A BLUR. ANGER.

I'M SO, SO SORRY.

...I DON'T KNOW WHERE IT WAS. NOT HERE. NOT ANYWHERE I KNOW.

SOMEPLACE... OTHER.

BUT MY SOUL-SELF WAS THERE. TRAPPED. HURT.

...AND ON TOP OF ALL *THAT*, EVERY LAST *ONE* OF US HAS A PROBLEM...

...GAR STRUGGLING WITH HIS CONDITION...

...RAVEN LOSING HER SOUL-SELF...

...MISS M GETTING HURT AND BEING FORCED TO REVEAL SOMETHING PAINFULLY PRIVATE...

...STEEL WORKING HERSELF TO *EXHAUSTION* TO FIND A WAY OUT OF THIS BECAUSE SHE KNOWS THE DATA SHE CARRIES MIGHT *SAVE* PLANET EARTH...

I HAVE ISSUES OF MY OWN.

A FEW DAYS BEFORE NIGHTWING WAS SHOT, I ATTENDED A FUNERAL.

ROY HARPER'S FUNERAL.*

*GREEN ARROW #45.
--PAUL

WHAT? OH MY GOD!

DONNA--

WHY DIDN'T YOU SAY ANY-THING?

I DIDN'T SAY ANYTHING BECAUSE IT *HURT.*

I LOVED HIM.

AND...IT FELT LIKE IT WAS JUST MORE *CRAP* FOR YOU TO DEAL WITH.

THAT WAS A MISTAKE.

THE OLD TITANS ARE DISAPPEARING OR DYING.

NIGHTWING CHOSE ME AS A LINK TO THE *ORIGINAL* TEAM'S SPIRIT.

SO I'M GOING TO BE *THAT.* STARTING *NOW.*

NO MORE LIES. NO MORE SECRETS.

WE ARE GOING TO STICK *TOGETHER.* WE ARE *NOT* GOING TO GIVE UP.

WE'RE GOING TO GET THE HELL *HOME, AND* SAVE THE WORLD, *AND* COMPLETE THE MISSION *NIGHTWING* CHOSE US FOR.

NO MATTER *WHAT.* BECAUSE WE'RE THE TITANS AND TITANS *NEVER* QUIT.

GAR? RAVEN? GO SEE IF YOU CAN PROCESS ANYTHING FOR FOOD...EVEN *BASIC* NUTRIENT COMPOUNDS.

STEEL? GET TO WORK ON THE BOOM ROOM'S DRIVE SYSTEMS.

A-ABSOLUTELY.

ON IT.

OKAY.

AND I--

YOU NEED TO REST.

I AM--WELL *ENOUGH* TO HELP.

IN SOME *SMALL* WAYS AT LEAST.

YOU MAKE A *FINE* LEADER, DONNA TROY.

OH HERA, *NO.* I WAS JUST TRYING TO RALLY--

WE *NEED* A LEADER.

IT WAS NEVER GOING TO BE ME. THOUGH I AM YOUR *LIAISON* TO THE *JUSTICE LEAGUE,* I NOW BELIEVE J'ONN J'ONZZ PUT ME ON THIS TEAM SO *YOU* COULD WATCH OVER *ME.*

WELL, I-- --WHAT THE?!

TITANS!

WHAT'S HAPPENING?

THAT *LIGHT!* WHAT THE *HELL*--

TITANS
#31

"THE SOURCE WALL.

"IT'S THE BEGINNING *AND THE* END OF CREATION ITSELF. A BARRIER THAT PROTECTS THE *GREATEST* SECRETS OF THE COSMOS.

"AND NOW, FOR THE FIRST TIME IN HISTORY, THERE'S A GREAT BIG *HOLE* IN IT.

"THE GREEN LANTERN CORPS HAS BEEN MONITORING THE RIFT* FOR ANY FURTHER DEGRADATION, READY IN CASE...WHO KNOWS *WHAT* COMES OUT.

"IT'S THE KIND OF RESPONSIBILITY THAT THE CORPS WAS MADE TO TACKLE...BUT THIS IS *BIG.*

"BIGGER THAN ANY THREAT WE COULD IMAGINE.

*AS SEEN IN *JUSTICE LEAGUE: NO JUSTICE.*

"AND NOT FOR NOTHING, BUT ONLY *I* REALLY KNOW *HOW* BIG...

"...BECAUSE I ONCE WENT *BEYOND* THE WALL."

*SEE *GREEN LANTERN: LIGHTS OUT.*

SORRY, GUYS. TALKING TOO MUCH.

HELPS ME CONCENTRATE, YOU KNOW?

NO, IT'S *VERY* INTERESTING, KYLE RAYNER.

KYLE... WHEN YOU WENT BEYOND THE WALL... WHAT DID YOU *SEE?*

HONESTLY... THERE ARE *NO* WORDS.

BUT IF IT COMES SPILLING INTO OUR UNIVERSE, THERE'S NO PUTTING THAT GENIE BACK IN THE BOTTLE.

THE OTHER SIDE

DAN ABNETT — writer
CLAYTON HENRY &
BRENT PEEPLES — pencils
CLAYTON HENRY &
DEXTER VINES — inks
MARCELO MAIOLO — colors
DAVE SHARPE — letters
CLAYTON HENRY &
IVAN PLASCENCIA — cover
ROB LEVIN — associate editor
PAUL KAMINSKI — editor
MARIE JAVINS — group editor

...SO, COME ON, RAYNER. WHAT *DID* YOU SEE ON THE OTHER SIDE OF THE SOURCE WALL?

EVERYTHING.

IT WAS... ...RAW, PRIMORDIAL *POWER. INFINITE* POWER.

MAYBE MORE THAN ANYONE--INCLUDING THE *LEAGUE* AND THE *CORPS*-- I KNOW IT NEEDS TO BE HELD AT *BAY* TO PRESERVE THE UNIVERSE.

EVEN WITH JUST THE CRACK IN THE WALL, ITS EFFECTS ON THE PLANET HAVE BEEN DANGEROUS.

THE TITANS HAVE BEEN CHARGED WITH PROTECTING THE PEOPLE FROM THOSE HOSTILE EFFECTS WHILE THE JUSTICE LEAGUE TACKLES THE BIGGER PICTURE.

I STILL CAN'T *BELIEVE* YOU'RE ALL BACK!

I THOUGHT WE'D *LOST* YOU!

WE WERE *LUCKY,* MR. RUBEL. IF KYLE HADN'T PICKED UP OUR SIGNAL, WE'D BE *DEAD* BY NOW.

DEAD, AND A *LONG* WAY AWAY.

YOU MISSED A *LOT.*

THE MEMORIES ARE A LITTLE FUZZY FOR SOME REASON? BUT I'M PRETTY SURE I WAS A FISH MONSTER FOR, LIKE, A *WHILE.**

CRAZY STUFF.

AFTER THE EVACUATION I BASICALLY JUST HUNG IN THE LAB, KEEPING OUT OF EVERYONE'S WAY...

...IT'S ONE THING TO SEE THE *JUSTICE LEAGUE* ON TV--

--I'VE HAD A LOT OF TIME ALONE TO THINK, AND WORRY...

*BETTER READ ALL OF *DROWNED EARTH* TO GET THE FULL STORY. --PAUL

I SHOULD GET BACK TO THE SOURCE WALL.

BEING BACK ON EARTH IS GREAT, BUT THE CORPS NEEDS ALL HANDS ON DECK.

I UNDERSTAND. THAT IS THE BIG PICTURE.

WISH I COULD STAY.

FEELS LIKE THE *REAL* FIGHT IS HAPPENING HERE.

I SHOULD REPORT IN TO THE LEAGUE.

COME WITH ME BEFORE YOU HEAD OUT.

MEDICAL BAY.

THIS *ISN'T* NECESSARY, MISS M.

A MEDI-SCAN? SERIOUSLY, I AM *NOT* GOING TO SPIN OUT AGAIN LIKE I DID ON THAT PLANET--

I WILL BE THE JUDGE OF THAT, GARFIELD.

YOU WERE *BADLY* AFFECTED BY SOURCE WALL ENERGY. WE NEED TO MAKE *CERTAIN* YOU ARE STABLE AGAIN.

BUT YOU GOT HURT, TOO, YOU KNOW.

I AM HEALING FAST AND MY STRENGTH IS RETURNING. JUST SIT THERE AND ALLOW THE SCAN TO RUN.

AND AS FOR *YOU*, RAVEN...

AS FOR ME WHAT?

I WANT TO MAKE SENSE OF THE *VISION* YOU EXPERIENCED... AND PERHAPS ASCERTAIN THE *LOCATION* OF YOUR MISSING SOUL-SELF.

WELL... ARE YOU FEELING UP TO THAT?

YOU WERE INJURED--

AS I ASSURED GARFIELD, MY VIGOR IS *RETURNING.*

AND I SENSE YOU ONLY EXPRESS CONCERN OUT OF *POLITENESS.*

I SAID IT BECAUSE IT'S WHAT PEOPLE ARE SUPPOSED TO SAY TO THEIR FRIENDS.

WITHOUT MY SOUL-SELF, I FEEL *NOTHING* ABOUT *ANYTHING.*

IT'S CLEARLY *DEBILITATING.*

YOU *ARE* MY FRIEND, AND I WANT TO *HELP.*

WH--WHAT ARE YOU DOING?

ATTUNING THE MIND-LINK, ONE-ON-ONE.

WHY?

TO EXAMINE YOUR MIND. THE VISION YOU HAD...

RIGHT, THAT.

MY SOUL-SELF HAS BEEN MISSING FOR WEEKS. WHY DID I GET A VISION NOW, ALL OF A SUDDE--

I *SEE* SOMETHING.

SO YOU'RE LEADING THE TEAM NOW?

WELL--

OF *COURSE* SHE IS.

DICK WOULD HAVE WANTED THAT.

ABOUT M'GANN... WE *KNOW* HER SECRET.

YOU SHOULD HAVE *TOLD* US SO WE COULD HAVE SUPPORTED HER BETTER.

WE'RE BABYSITTING *HER,* NOT THE OTHER WAY AROUND.

IT'S A DANGEROUS TIME FOR WHITE MARTIANS. J'ONN HAD M'GANN MASQUERADE AS A GREEN MARTIAN TO *PROTECT* HER TRUE NATURE.

HE PLACED HER WITH YOUR TEAM TO KEEP HER SAFE.

PROTECT HER SECRET. NO ONE CAN KNOW.

OKAY, BUT--

DONNA TROY TO THE TITANS' CHAMBER! URGENT!

GOTTA GO.

WHAT'S SO UR--
--OH.
HOLY--
THAT.
THAT'S SO URGENT.
SOMETHING'S HAPPENING TO BEAST BOY. I THINK...
...I THINK HE'S BEEN POSSESSED.
I'LL CUT HIM THE HELL OUT OF THAT--
NO, DONNA.
IT'S A PSYCHIC MANIFESTATION.
DISTURBING HIM COULD BE CATASTROPHIC... LIKE WAKING A SLEEPWALKER.
T-TITANS...

WHAT?

GUYS?

WHAT JUST HAPPENED? I FEEL KINDA *FUNKY*...

YOU DON'T *WANT* TO KNOW.

STEADY NOW...

I KNOW WE THOUGHT WE *SEALED* UNEARTH, BUT I WANT A WORKING PLAN TO GET BACK IN THERE *FAST*.

WE CAN'T IGNORE THIS.

UM, QUESTION?

WHAT'S "UNEARTH"? AND DOES THIS KIND OF THING HAPPEN A *LOT*?

UNEARTH WAS A REALM SPONTANEOUSLY *MANIFESTED* FROM A MAN'S IMAGINATION BY SOURCE ENERGY, KYLE RAYNER.

IT IS BASICALLY A WORK OF *FANTASY FICTION* BROUGHT TO *LIFE*.

RAVEN? THIS DEVELOPMENT OFFERS *YOU* HOPE FOR RECOVERY.

THAT'S... THAT'S GOOD.

BUT REENTERING UNEARTH IS *PROBLEMATIC*.

I DELIBERATELY CLOSED IT AND *DISCONNECTED* IT FROM THE MULTIVERSE.

YEAH, BUT THERE *COULD* BE A WAY! BOOM ROOM TECH *COULD* OPEN A DOOR--

TRANSDIMENSIONALLY?

RIGHT! AND BECAUSE UNEARTH IS *MADE* FROM SOURCE ENERGY...

...WE CAN USE THE *RUBEL-IRONS CAPACITOR* TO CHARGE THE GATE AND KEEP IT *ENERGETICALLY STABLE!*

WELL... I CAN WILL UP ANY PORTAL ARCHITECTURE OR POWER MODERATOR YOU'D NEED, BUT HOW DO WE NAVIGATE INTER-DIMENSIONALLY?

WE USE THE *OCEAN LORDS' DATA!*

MASSIVELY ADVANCED *SUBSPACE NAVIGATIONAL TOOLS!* WE CAN *PLOT* THE INTERSTITIAL FIX!

THIS COULD *WORK!*

THEY'RE USING *WORDS*, BUT NOT IN *ANY* WAY I UNDERSTAND.

THEN AGAIN, I *STILL* DON'T UNDERSTAND WHY WE'RE ALL COVERED IN KETCHUP...

SHORT VERSION--WE HAVE A *PLAN*, GAR.

OUR FIRST CHANCE TO GET *AHEAD* OF THE BLOOD CULT.

AND IT GIVES US AN OPPORTUNITY TO RECOVER YOUR SOUL-SELF, *TOO*, RACHEL.

AH.

FANTASTIC.

TITANS
#32

THE CULT OF BLOOD SEEKS TO **SEIZE CONTROL** OF THE RED.

IT SEEKS TO USE IT FOR ITS **OWN** ENDS.

IT **MUST** BE STOPPED, OR **ALL LIFE** WILL FALL TO THE CULT'S POWER.

GARFIELD? **GARFIELD!**

HOW IS THE CULT **DOING** THIS?

IT INTENDS TO ASSAULT THE RED THROUGH A **BRAND-NEW** ASPECT OF LIFE, A WORLD NEWBORN INTO THE **MULTIVERSE.**

A PLACE CALLED **UNEARTH.**

BUT THE CULT'S NEVER HAD **THAT** KIND OF POWER.

GARFIELD, WHO IS **DOING** THIS?

MOTHER IS.

MOTHER IS!

NNYYYAAARRRRGGH—

IT'S THE BLOOD THAT BINDS US.

FRESNO, THEN.

HERE IS WHERE I DIE.

THE FIRST TIME.

MY NAME WAS SONYA TARINKA.

I WAS PERSECUTED BY MY FAMILY AND MY GOVERNMENT AND FLED TO THE UNITED STATES FOR HELP.

FOR ASYLUM.

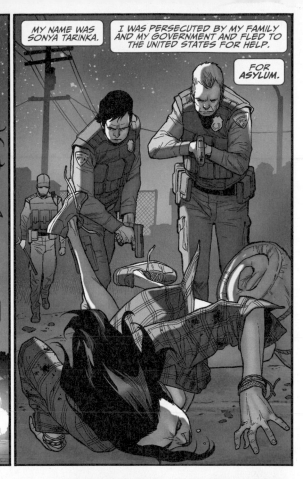

BUT I AM PERSECUTED HERE, TOO.

ALL MY LIFE I HAVE BEEN BEATEN DOWN BY OTHERS... I AM POWERLESS. I FEEL POWERLESS.

I AM YOUNG. I AM EDUCATED... BUT THIS MAN TELLS ME I AM ILLEGAL.

I HAVE NO HOME HERE. I HAVE NO HOME ANYWHERE.

I AM FOREVER AT THE MERCY OF OTHERS.

HERE IS WHERE I DIE.

GET IN.

DAN ABNETT
WRITER
CLAYTON
HENRY
ARTIST
MARCELO
MAIOLO
COLORS
DAVE
SHARPE
LETTERS
CLAYTON HENRY & DEAN WHITE COVER
ROB LEVIN ASSOCIATE EDITOR   PAUL KAMINSKI EDITOR
MARIE JAVINS
GROUP EDITOR

IT DOESN'T MATTER.

WE ARE HIS WHILE WE STAY HERE.

WE HAVE BEDS. A ROOF. THERE IS FOOD.

HE DOES NOT CHASE US WITH *DOGS* OR TRY TO *DEPORT* US.

SO WE EMBRACE IT ALL.

JUST LIKE THOSE BROTHERS AND SISTERS WHO HAVE COME BEFORE US.

AND WE PUT UP WITH HIS...ECCENTRICITIES.

UNTIL IT BECOMES CLEAR THAT--WHEN IT COMES TO ETERNAL LIFE-- IT'S ALL ABOUT HIM.

AND I BEGIN TO WONDER IF A BED, AND FOOD, AND HIS PROMISES ARE WORTH STAYING HERE FOR.

CR
REEEAKK

Hmm.

SISTER
SONYA.

YOU
SENT FOR ME,
BROTHER.

YOU LOOK
DISAPPOINTED.

IT'S JUST A
COSTUME.

THE POWER
IS HERE, SISTER
SONYA.

IT HAS BEEN
FOR SEVEN
CENTURIES.

OF
COURSE.

THE POWER TO TURN OUR ANCIENT BELIEFS INTO *FACT*. TO FINALLY *DELIVER* ON THE DOCTRINES OF OUR CHURCH.

TO CONTROL THIS WORLD, AND ALL *POSSIBLE* WORLDS, AS *DIVINE* CREATURES.

IT WAS LIKE WATCHING AN ORANGUTAN TRY TO RECITE SHAKESPEARE. HE STUMBLED UPON SOME SOUNDS, WITH NO IDEA WHAT WAS BEING SAID.

I *NEED* A SCIENTIST, SONYA. SOMEONE TO LEAD A SPECIAL MISSION.

WE MUST OBTAIN AND *MASTER* THIS POWER BEFORE *ANYONE* ELSE.

BEFORE THE *METAHUMAN* HEROES DO.

O-OKAY, BROTHER.

THE WINDOW OF OPPORTUNITY IS *SMALL*.

I, UHM...

TELL ME WHAT TO DO AND I WILL DO IT.

LET'S DRINK TO THAT.

IT WAS IN THAT MOMENT, LOOKING INTO BROTHER BLOOD'S EYES DRIPPING WITH INSANITY, THAT I RESOLVED TO BREAK FREE.

I DID NOT BELIEVE HIS TALK OF A "COMING GREAT POWER" ANY MORE THAN I BELIEVED THE REST OF HIS MYSTICAL PROMISES.

BUT I WOULD SELECT MISSIONARIES, THE FIVE RECRUITS BROUGHT IN ALONGSIDE ME.

AND BEGIN THE RESEARCH...

YOU TALK *NONSENSE*, SONYA.

JUST LIKE THE BROTHER DID.

AND WHAT IS WITH THIS STUPID *COSTUME*?

IT'S *NOT* NONSENSE, PADMESH.

THE BROTHER'S POWER DEPENDED ON *BELIEF*. ON *US* BELIEVING IN *HIM*.

NOW I CAN TAKE THE RED AND MAKE *EVERYONE* BELIEVE. EVERYONE *EVERYWHERE*.

ON THIS WORLD, AND ON THE *OTHER* WORLDS I NOW KNOW EXIST.

A *MULTIVERSE* OF UNWAVERING FAITHFUL, LINKED BY THE RED, BELIEVING IN *US*.

NO ONE COULD EVER TAKE FROM US AGAIN, MY FRIENDS. THE CRUELTY OF THIS WORLD COULD BE *WIPED* FROM *EXISTENCE*.

THAT IS THE ASCENSION THE BROTHER PROMISED. MORE THAN HE *EVER* KNEW.

BUT... EVEN IF THIS *IS* TRUE, WHICH I DOUBT...

...THE CHURCH IS *GONE*.

IN MY ABSENCE, THE METAHUMAN *TEEN TITANS* ASSAULTED OUR RETREAT.

THEY CAPTURED THE BROTHER AND BROKE UP THE CHURCH.

ONLY MY MISSIONARIES AND I AVOIDED THIS FATE BECAUSE WE WERE *OFF-SITE*, CONDUCTING RESEARCH ACROSS THE COUNTRY.

WE ARE *ALL* THAT REMAINS OF THE CHURCH OF BLOOD.

ARTEM, LENA AND THE OTHERS THINK WE ARE DONE. THAT WE HAVE NO LEADER.

TIME IS SHORT.

WE LEARN ALL WE CAN ABOUT THE SOURCE ENERGY THAT GIVES ME THESE GIFTS, AND ITS EFFECTS ON THIS PLANET.

WE LEARN TO HARNESS IT, AND WEAPONIZE IT.

AND WE HAVE COMPETITION.

THE TITANS

CHARGED BY THE INFAMOUS JUSTICE LEAGUE TO GUARD THE EARTH AGAINST SOURCE ENERGY FALLOUT.

THE LATEST ITERATION OF THE METAHUMAN GANG THAT HAS THWARTED THE BROTHER'S CHURCH MORE THAN ANY OTHER.

WE USE THE SCRYING GLASSES TO WATCH THEM.

I REALIZE HOW CLOSE THEY'RE GETTING TO BEATING US IN THIS RACE TO MASTER THE SOURCE ENERGY'S EFFECTS.

TITANS
#33

ON IT. THIS IS SOME *CRAZY* PETER JACKSON STUFF RIGHT HERE.

THIS, BROTHER, IS JUST *ANOTHER DAY* IN THE TITANS!

INTO THE BLEED PART ONE

DAN ABNETT WRITER • **BRUNO REDONDO** ARTIST
HI-FI COLORS • **DAVE SHARPE** LETTERS
MICO SUAYAN & BLOND COVER
ROB LEVIN ASSOCIATE EDITOR
PAUL KAMINSKI EDITOR • **MARIE JAVINS** GROUP EDITOR

YEAH, HOW'RE WE *DOING* ON THAT FRONT? FEELS LIKE WE'RE GETTING OUR *BUTTS HANDE--*

AMONGST OTHER THINGS. LIKE *SAVING THE MULTIVERSE.*

REASSURE YOURSELF, RAVEN. WE ARE HERE TO *RESCUE YOUR SOUL-SELF.*

GUYS! CHAPTER SIXTEEN...

...THEY WERE, AFTER ALL, CREATED WITH BUT A *SINGLE* DUTY. *BORDER DEFENSE.*

LOATH THOUGH I *AM* TO TRUST A WORK OF *FANTASY* FICTION FOR GUIDANCE.

YOU *DROVE* 'EM OFF? *COOL.*

FEEL LIKE I SHOULD BE *DISHING OUT XP* ABOUT NOW.

MISS M'S *RIGHT,* THOUGH. THE URKESH READ AS PRETTY *SIMPLE* IN THE BOOKS. *UNDER-WRITTEN.* JUST *PLOT DEVICES.*

WHICH, I GUESS, MEANS IN REALITY THEY WILL BE *INCREDIBLY* SINGULAR IN PURPOSE.

UNDERSTOOD, BEN.

LET'S KEEP MOVING BEFORE THEY REGROUP.

ONE GUY MADE ALL THIS? A *WHOLE WORLD?*

YES, KYLE RAYNER. *INVOLUNTARILY.*

SOURCE ENERGY ALTERED THE MIND OF THE AUTHOR AND BROUGHT HIS *ENTIRE* WORLD INTO BEING.

WILD. I KNOW *ALL* ABOUT CREATING BY WILL, BUT A *WORLD...?* WITH CREATURES AND CULTURES AND--

ERNEST HINTON WAS AMAZED, *TOO.* SEEING HIS IMAGINATION BECOME *REAL.*

IT WAS FORMED FROM *PURE* SOURCE ENERGY, WHICH IS WHY IT'S SO *VALUABLE* TO THE BLOOD CULT.

WE MUST MOVE QUICKLY. WHERE TO NEXT, BEN RUBEL?

'KAY. SOOO, I'M THINKING YOU SHOULD HEAD TOWARD THE *MOUNTAINS.*

YOU *SEE* MOUNTAINS, RIGHT?

THERE'S A FORTRESS UP THERE CALLED THE *NORTHERN HOLD...*

PRINCE OF UNEARTH

HOW IS THE PLACE DEFENDED?

I GOT THIS.

HEY, ROOTKIN! *HERE'S* A RIDDLE...

...ONE RING TO BIND YOU ALL...

...AND TURN YOU INTO *MATCHSTICKS.* WANNA SEE IT IN ACTION?

HELL NO!

MIND HOW YOU GO!

SORRY TO BOTHER YOU, DUDE!

I AM GONNA MAKE LIKE A TREE...

SMOOTH.

YEAH. I WAS REALLY *TOLKIEN* THEIR LANGUAGE.

KYLE'S SURE DEVELOPING *BAD HOBBITS!*

WHAT?

OH, IT'S FUNNY WHEN *KYLE* DOES IT!

TITANS!

THIS IS A *VITAL* MISSION. THE BLOOD CULT INTENDS TO CORRUPT THE *PARLIAMENT OF THE RED,* THE SPIRIT THAT BINDS *ALL ORGANIC* LIFE.

THE FATE OF *WORLDS* IS AT STAKE...

UGHNNNKK!

AAAAHHH!

GRRRAAAAAKKKK!!

NAT? NAT! YOU OKAY?

I'M OKAY. SHAKEN UP, BUT OKAY.

GRIFFIN-GIRL HERE SURE PACKS A *PUNCH!* I THINK *SHE'S* THEIR LEADER--

UGFF!

YEAH, SHE--

OH MY GOD...

TITANS
#34

WELCOME TO UNEARTH.

I'VE TAKEN GREAT TIME AND EFFORT TO BRING YOU HERE. I REQUIRE YOUR PARTICULAR SKILL SETS.

KYLE RAYNER, THE ONLY LIVING BEING TO CROSS BEYOND THE SOURCE WALL. YOUR KNOWLEDGE WILL SHOW ME THE *BLEED SPACE* THAT CONNECTS THE ENTIRE MULTIVERSE...

...AND NATASHA IRONS, YOU CAN NAVIGATE SPACE-TIME AND CHANNEL SOURCE ENERGY... GIVING ME ACCESS TO *EVERYWHERE*.

I INTEND TO *FLOOD* THE MULTI-VERSE WITH THE POWER OF *THE RED*, YOU SEE.

YYIIIKKK!

LET'S DRINK TO THAT.

HEY--! NOW HANG ON! WHAT--?

WE'LL NEVER HELP YOU, MOTHER BLOOD, YOU MURDERING PIECE OF—

UH BUH-BUH-BUH!

STEEL, GREEN LANTERN... PLEASE.

YOU ARE HARDLY IN A POSITION TO DECLINE.

INTO THE BLEED

PART TWO

DAN ABNETT WRITER
BRUNO REDONDO ARTIST
MARCELO MAIOLO COLORS
DAVE SHARPE LETTERS
MICO SUAYAN & BLOND COVER
ROB LEVIN ASSOCIATE EDITOR
PAUL KAMINSKI EDITOR
MARIE JAVINS GROUP EDITOR

I HAVE NO IDEA WHO THIS "RAVEN" IS.

YOU ARE!

Y-YOU... AND SO IS THIS PRISONER! I DON'T—

WHAT HAVE THEY DONE TO YOU?

...THE *FULL MIGHT* OF OUR BORDER GUARD HAS THEM PINNED IN THE NORTH WASTE.

I AM RETURNING TO THE FIELD OF WAR...

"...TO *END* THEIR LIVES."

THIS WAS A TRAP FROM THE VERY *START*, AND I THINK I WALKED US INTO IT.

WE'RE FACING OVERWHELMING NUMBERS...

...AND WITH MISS MARTIAN AND RAVEN BOTH INJURED--

--THE TEAM'S HARDLY AT FULL STRENGTH.

I UNDERESTIMATED THIS WORLD'S CAPABILITIES.

ALL I KNEW WAS UNEARTH WAS *CRUCIAL* TO MOTHER BLOOD'S PLANS...

...BECAUSE IT'S A BLANK SLATE. AN UNTAINTED WORLD NEWLY CREATED IN THE MULTIVERSE...

...A PERFECT ALTAR FOR THE CULT TO PERFORM ITS RITUAL OF MULTIVERSAL CORRUPTION.

AND WE CAN'T HOPE TO--

WHERE ARE *KYLE* AND *STEEL*? HAS *ANYONE* SEEN THEM?

TWO OF OUR BIGGEST HITTERS MISSING IN ACTION, A THIRD JUST KNOCKED DOWN...

WE NEED HELP... OR A MIRACLE.

HALL OF JUSTICE. EARTH.

THE FORTRESS OF THE NORTHERN HOLD. UNEARTH.

IF YOU NEED TO SCREAM, I DO UNDERSTAND.

WH-WHAT THE...HELL...ARE YOU TRYING T-TO DO?!

KYLE... CAN I CALL YOU KYLE?

YOU SEE, KYLE, MY CULT... THOUGH I DISLIKE THAT WORD... HAS TRADITIONALLY WORSHIPPED THE PARLIAMENT OF THE RED.

THAT IS TO SAY, THE PRIMAL FORCE OF ALL ORGANIC LIFE.

WE HAVE ALWAYS BEEN ITS SERVANTS.

MY WHOLE LIFE, I HAVE BEEN FORCED TO OBEY OTHERS.

THE WHOLE WORLD HAS DONE NOTHING BUT HOUND ME AND HURT ME AND BLEED ME DRY.

WELL, NOW IT'S MY TURN.

I EXPERIENCED THE TOTALITY, THE SOURCE. ITS POWERS BATHED ME...

...AND ALLOWED ME TO TAKE CONTROL OF THE RED.

GO AHEAD, IF IT HELPS.

THE MAP IS FORMING, DROP BY DROP, BUT I CAN TASTE HOW PAINFUL THE PROCESS IS FOR YOU BOTH.

PLEASE EXPRESS YOUR SUFFERING, IF IT EASES YOUR BURDEN.

TITANS

#35

TRAVESTY? WHAT HAVE YOU *DONE*? *TRAVESTY*?

JUST *DON'T*.

GIVE ME A MOMENT. I HAVE KILLED MY *CREATOR*.

BUT, TRAVESTY--

DON'T!

I HAD TO. MAKER ERNEST... HE WAS GOING TO--

I *HAD* TO.

I *KNOW* IT HURTS, TRAVESTY...

I KNOW HOW IT FEELS TO BE POWERLESS. *YEARNING* TO ASSERT YOUR POWER OVER THOSE WHO *CONTROL* YOU.

BUT IT IS LIBERATING WHEN YOU FINALLY *FIND* THAT STRENGTH.

IT HURTS, BUT YOU DID THE *RIGHT* THING. A *BRAVE* THING.

NOW *COLLECT* YOUR WITS. I NEED YOU *STRONG*.

OUR FIRST ORDER OF BUSINESS IS TO ENSURE THE TITANS HAVE NOT BREACHED OUR LINES.

YOUR
BETRAYAL WAS
POINTLESS.

THE
GATES OF THE
MULTIVERSE
WILL OPEN
FOR ME...

KTZZ

THE GREAT HALL.

WHY HAS
THE GLASS GONE
DARK? WHERE DID
THE PICTURE
GO?

I DON'T
KNOW. MOTHER
SHOULD--

OH. *THAT'S* NOT
PROMISING...

KRRRRRRM

TITANS

INTO THE BLEED
FINALE

DAN ABNETT WRITER BRUNO REDONDO ARTIST
MARCELO MAIOLO COLORS
REDONDO and ALEJANDRO SANCHEZ COVER
DAVE SHARPE LETTERS
ROB LEVIN ASSOCIATE EDITOR
PAUL KAMINSKI EDITOR
JAMIE S. RICH GROUP EDITOR

WHAT

IS

HAPPENING?

A FUNDAMENTAL LOSS OF STRUCTURAL INTEGRITY.

UNEARTH IS... UNRAVELING.

WE HAVE TO REACH MOTHER BLOOD! WE--

I CAN READ HER FROM *HERE*, DONNA. HER THOUGHTS AND FEELINGS AS HOT AS *MAGMA*.

SHE'S *GOT WHAT SHE WANTS...*

"...AND SHE'S *WON.*"

I CAN SEE ETERNITY...

"--HOW CAN WE SAVE WORLDS WHEN WE CAN'T EVEN SAVE OURSELVES?"

I AM RENEWED. REUNITED. MY POWER SINGS INSIDE ME, AMPLIFIED BY THIS FANTASTIC WORLD.

I CAN FEEL MOTHER BLOOD UNLEASHING HER UNHOLY POWER IN THE CHAMBER DEAD AHEAD.

MAYBE THIS IS MY MOMENT. THE MOMENT NIGHTWING CHOSE ME FOR.

OH.

RAYNER!

HIT IT WITH *EVERYTHING* YOU GOT, STEEL!

SSHHRAAAKKKKKOOOOOOMMFFF

WHOA.

THMMMMFFFFFF

BECAUSE THE *BLEED*—

BLOCKS SOURCE ENERGY. AND THAT'S WHAT HER POWER WAS *BASED* ON.

SO... MOTHER BLOOD'S IN THE BLEED?

FOREVER.

WITHOUT THE *RIGHT PEOPLE* TO OPEN A DOOR, SHE CAN'T *GET OUT*.

SAME REASON *GARFIELD* IS BACK TO NORMAL.

I'M CUTE AGAIN!

WOO!

EXPOSURE *PURGED* THE SOURCE ENERGY FROM HIM.

YOU AREN'T COMING BACK *WITH US*, ARE YOU?

NO, YOUNG LADY. I'D PREFER TO STAY.

BUT, MR. HINTON—

I APPRECIATE ALL YOU'VE DONE FOR ME, TITANS. BELIEVE ME.

BUT I THINK THERE ARE MORE *STORIES* TO TELL HERE IN UNEARTH.

VARIANT COVER GALLERY

TITANS #29 variant cover
by YASMINE PUTRI

TITANS #30 variant cover
by YASMINE PUTRI

TITANS #31 variant cover
by PHILIP TAN and ELMER SANTOS

TITANS #33 variant cover
by TYLER KIRKHAM and ARIF PRIANTO

TYLER KIRKHAM

TITANS #34 variant cover
by TYLER KIRKHAM and ARIF PRIANTO

TITANS #35 variant cover
by RAFA SANDOVAL and ULISES ARREOLA

TITANS #36 variant cover
by FRANCIS MANAPUL

Blood Brothers

- Ancient looking, not slick and modern
- Ritualistic touches, like metal skull/tooth/horn mask
- Combat focussed with armor on key areas to help with blocking but overall light and easy to move in

Scabbards are attached under the hooded shoulder parts to keep the design neat. The swords are short and European in design to contrast with all the Asian design so prevailant in comics.

Blades, crossguard, and pommel are the same golden metal as the armor and mask.

I'm shying away from the Blood Brothers or their weapons having any sort of glowing or magical look. Though they are more powerful than standard cultists, I like the idea they are fanatical zealots who are well trained and not so much magically helped.

BLOOD VESSELS character studies by BRANDON PETERSON
COMMANDER LENORE character studies by BRUNO REDONDO

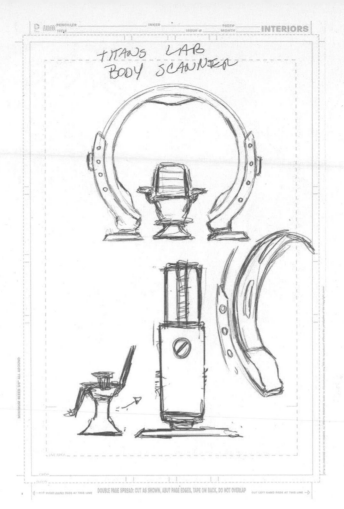

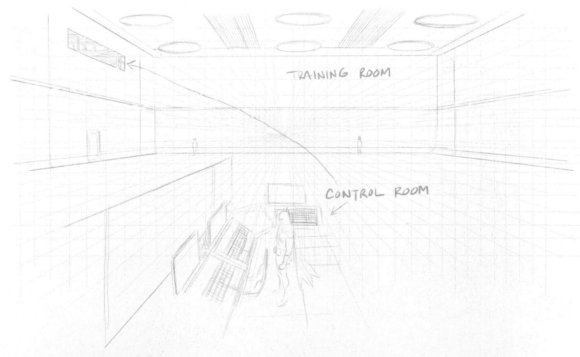

HALL OF JUSTICE LAB SCANNER design sketch by BRENT PEEPLES
HALL OF JUSTICE TRAINING ROOM design sketch by CLAYTON HENRY

TITANS #29 cover sketches by BRANDON PETERSON

TITANS #30 cover sketches by BEN OLIVER

TITANS #31 and **#32** cover sketches by CLAYTON HENRY

TITANS #33 and **#34** cover sketches by MICO SUAYAN

TITANS #35 and **#36** cover sketches by BRUNO REDONDO

Sketches for an unused cover to **TITANS #29** by BRANDON PETERSON

Unused cover to **TITANS #29** by BRANDON PETERSON

TITANS #29 page 16 line art by MINKYU JUNG and JOHN DELL

TITANS #31 page 20 line art by BRENT PEEPLES and DEXTER VINES

TITANS #35 page 20 line art by BRUNO REDONDO